Tea Club

1

Story & Art by
PMBQ

dedicated to

Benedict Norbert Wong

visionary, mentor, and beloved friend

1943 - 2005

your inspiration lives on

Tea Club
Vol. 1

Story and Art by Phuong-Mai Bui-Quang ("PMBQ")

Japanese Kanji writing in "Happy Birthday, Hana Neko" by Christian "Ian" Sy

Official Tea Club website:
http://www.teaclubcomic.com

The majority of the content in this book was published online and in its own comic book mini-series from 2001-2003.

Lettering fonts provided courtesy of Blambot
http://www.blambot.com

Special thanks to Simon Jones, Marcial Pelayo, Jr. and Marissa Pelayo.

To my webcomic readers, fans, dear friends and family,
thanks for all your love and support!

Published by P.M.B.Q. Studios
P.O. Box 111616
Campbell, CA 95011-1616
http://www.pmbq.com

First Printing, Spring 2006
ISBN: 1-59971-581-3

10 9 8 7 6 5 4 3 2 1

Printed in the United States of America

TABLE OF CONTENTS

Tea Club

the first
MEETING

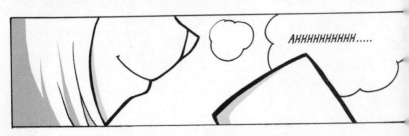

HANA.

FOR JUST ONCE, COULD YOU *SHUT UP* AND DRINK YOUR TEA LIKE A NORMAL PERSON?!

...

SORRY KRIS... I CAN'T HELP IT!

FOR AS LONG AS I CAN REMEMBER, TEA HAS BEEN AN IMPORTANT PART OF MY UPBRINGING.

NOW THAT I'M A FRESHMAN HERE AT TALLAN UNIVERSITY, WHO KNOWS WHAT WILL HAPPEN?!

I NEED THE COMFORTS OF TEA NOW MORE THAN EVER!

IN FACT...

I FOUND OUT THAT THERE'S A TEA CLUB ON CAMPUS!

Tea Club
MEETING TO...

FIRST MEETING IS TODAY! ISN'T THAT COOL?!

MAYBE THE PRESIDENT WILL BE SOME REALLY HUNKY GUY WHO LOVES TEA JUST AS MUCH AS I DO...

I'LL HAVE MY FIRST COLLEGE ROMANCE!

"TEA CLUB"?

I'VE NEVER HEARD OF THIS BEFORE.

HANEKO, I REALLY THINK YOU SHOULD BE CAREFU

OMIGOSH, LOOKITTHETIME

UMM...
O.K. I'LL GIVE IT A SHOT.

HI, NICE TO MEET YOU! MY NAME IS HANA NEKO (BUT YOU CAN CALL ME HANEKO).

I CAME TO JOIN THE TEA CLUB...

...WOULD YOU KNOW ANYTHING ABOUT IT?

YAWN

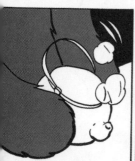

15

HEY, YOU DID POUR **SCALDING HOT TEA** ON ME.

(AND LET'S NOT FORGET THAT LOVELY RIGHT UPPERCUT OF YOURS.)

SIGH

WE'RE EVEN NOW...BUT IT'S TOO BAD ABOUT THE TEA. A WHOLE POT OF MINT TEA, *RUINED!*

MINT TEA?!

MMM....MINT TEA....

WAIT A MINUTE. IS THIS BEAR...TALKING?!

WELL, I GUESS IT WASN'T A COMPLETE WASTE.

I AM *VERY IMPRESSED* WITH YOUR REFLEXES, MS. HANA NEKO.

THIS IS JUST THE BEGINNING.

SO *SIP* TURNS OUT *SIP* THAT THE PRESIDENT *SIP* IS *SIP* THIS *SIP* BEAR...

SIP

WHOA.

YOU MEAN MR. BEAR?

WAIT, YOU *YOU KNOW ABOUT HIM?!*

TOTALLY!

WE HAD FRESHMAN SEMINAR TOGETHER LAST YEAR!

BUT THE RUMOR IS THAT HE'S BEEN AROUND TALLAN UNIVERSITY FOR QUITE A WHILE...

T.U.
DEAN'S LIST

29

31

HEY, HE'S *CUTE.*

DAMMIT! KRIS IS HOLDING OUT ON ME *AGAIN!* WHY DIDN'T SHE TELL ME ABOUT THIS GUY?

UNLESS... MAYBE *SHE* LIKES HIM!

WHOA, ALMOST FORGOT MY MANNERS.

HANA, MEET MY BEST FRIEND, *KEI OKUMA.*

WE'RE ON THE VARSITY CROSS-COUNTRY TEAM TOGETHER.

HAJIME-MASHITE*, HANA!

*NICE TO MEET YOU (FOR THE FIRST TIME).

KEI, THIS IS MY ROOMMATE, HANA NEKO.

HE'S CUTE HE'S CUTE HE'S CUTE

D-DOUZO YOROSHIKU* KEI.

*THE PLEASURE IS M

KRIS TOLD ME YOU WERE RAISED IN JAPAN.

YEAH! MY PARENTS ARE ORIGINALLY FROM FELIS, BUT THEY MET AND MARRIED IN JAPAN.

SO WHAT BRINGS YOU TO TALLAN U.?

I HEARD THAT T ALLAN HAD A GOOD PHYSICAL TRAINING PROGRAM,

SO I DECIDED TO COME AND STUDY IN THE U.S.

I WANTED TO TRAVEL, TOO!

REALLY!

I'M PRE-MED MYSELF.

OH! SO YOU KNOW ABOUT PROFESSOR D'ARBY'S *WORLD OF CELLS* LECTURE?!

HAHAHA!

I ALWAYS FELL ASLEEP IN THAT ONE!

EXCUSE ME...

THERE ARE THREE PEOPLE IN THIS COVERSATION, YES?!

AWW, KRIS, YOU'RE NOT BITTER 'CUZ YOU'RE STILL UNDECLARED, ARE YOU?

FE SUA

WHAT?!!? NO!!!

WHOA, IS THAT TRUE, KRIS? DON'T YOU KNOW WHAT YOU'RE GOING TO DO ONCE YOU GRADUATE?

KEII!! SEE WHAT YOU STARTED?!

HEY, DON'T LOOK AT ME, HANA'S A PRETTY SMART COOKIE.

*OOD DAY, MR. BEAR.
**KEI'S LAST NAME, OKUMA, MEANS BIG BEAR.

SO TELL ME, HANEKO.

GOT ANY PLANS FOR THE WEEKEND?

ACTUALLY, I WAS GOING TO--

zip~

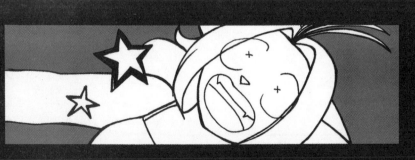

43

I--

UM..

I'M REALLY SORRY. I GOT CARRIED AWAY.

BOW.

HAH!

POM.

WHEN I FIRST SAW YOUR REFLEXES, I KNEW THAT YOU WOULD BE PERFECT FOR THE CEREMONIAL BATTLE.

WAIT A SEC.

YOU NEVE EVEN BOTHE TO TELL M WHAT TH IS.

OH!

WELL, IT ALL BEGAN MANY YEARS AGO...

ONE DAY, TEA MASTER
HAYAKAWA
HAD A TEA
CEREMONY WITH
A GOOD
FRIEND,
GENERAL
MURO.

ON THAT PARTICULAR DAY, THERE ALSO HAPPENED TO BE A GROUP OF PEASANTS JUST OUTSIDE THEIR HUT, CUTTING DOWN TREES FOR FIREWOOD.

CRAK!

HO! THAT'S A BIG ONE!

CRRRRRRRASHA

AS A RESULT OF THOSE PEASANTS, A MINOR MISHAP OCCURRED...

HAYAKAWA-SAN!

...AND THE TEA CEREMONY WAS INTERRUPTED.

45

THOSE PEASANTS WILL PAY FOR RUINING THIS CEREMONY!

RELAX, HIMURO-SAN.

THERE'S LITTLE HARM DONE... AND I WAS STILL ABLE TO SERVE YOU THE TEA.

OH!

PLEASE, DRINK IT, AND SEE FOR YOURSELF.

VERY WELL.

SIP!

HAYAKAWA-SAN, YOU ARE A TRUE TEA MASTER!

IT'S AS IF OUR CEREMONY WAS NEVER DISTURBED!

HIMURO-SAN WAS VERY IMPRESSED BY HIS FRIEND'S STRONG STATE OF MIND, ABLE TO PRESERVE THE TEA CEREMONY IN SUCH DISASTROUS CIRCUMSTANCES.

46

IMPRESSED, THAT HE BEGAN TO PURPOSEFULLY STAGE CATASTROPHES DURING THEIR TEA CEREMONIES, TO TEST YAKAWA-SAN'S ABILITIES.

AND THUS, THE CEREMONIAL BATTLE WAS BORN!

TODAY'S CEREMONIAL BATTLE CONSISTS OF TWO CHALLENGERS, ONE DEFENDER, AND ONE JUDGE. THE DEFENDER MUST COMPLETE THE TRADITIONAL JAPANESE TEA CEREMONY BY SERVING A SINGLE CUP OF TEA TO THE JUDGE.

MEANWHILE, THE CHALLENGERS HAVE ALMOST FREE REIGN IN ATTACKING THE DEFENDER.

IF THE CHALLENGER SUCCESSFULLY SERVES THE TEA, THEIR SCHOOL WINS. IF SHE CANNOT SERVE THE JUDGE, THEY LOSE.

IF THE TEA IS SERVED AND THE JUDGE DOESN'T LIKE IT--

I'M SORRY, MR. BEAR.

IT MUST SOUND SILLY.

I ACTUALLY DREAMED ABOUT A PLACE WHERE PEOPLE WOULD GATHER AND ENJOY TEA.

WORK@ HOME

Tea Club
MEETING TODAY
ROOM 326

SPAIN TOUR

WHEN I SAW YOUR FLYER, I THOUGHT MY DREAM HAD FINALLY COME TRUE!

BUT THIS.

THIS ISN'T A DREAM AT ALL.

I'M SUCH A TYPICAL NAIVE FRESHMAN!

OR MAYBE I'M JUST A *TYPICAL IDIOT.*

WHEN I SAW YOU ON THAT FIRST DAY, I SENSED YOUR POWERFUL BATTLE SPIRIT.

WOW, THAT'S SOME AURA... OR MAYBE IT'S JUST THE TEA.

AFTER WITNESSING YOUR SUPERB DISPLAY OF REFLEXES, I KNEW WE'D BE AN UNSTOPPABLE TEA CLUB.

MAYBE EVEN TAKE THE GOLDEN CUP!

I NEVER THOUGHT ABOUT HOW YOU FELT, THOUGH.

I PROBABLY CAN'T SAY IT ENOUGH, HANA...

I'M REALLY SORRY.

I HOP THAT YC BE ABLE FORGIVE SOMED.

DEEP BOW~··

I CAN'T FORCE YOU TO STAY IN THE TEA CLUB, SO...

....

...YOU'RE FREE TO GO.

53

I GOTTA TELL MANAMI ABOUT ALL THIS STUFF.

BEST FRIEND FROM JAPAN, MANAMI!

WRITE WRITE

Happy Birthday,

HANA NEKO

Dear Manami-chan,

How's my best buddy doing? Tokyo U. life treating you well?

I miss you A LOT. I'm doing OK, though. You know me, one cup of tea and my world is right again

It's my second week here at school, and it sure is different from home in Japan.

For one thing, one of the students here is a BEAR. That's right, big, four paws, furry, snout and all!

And get this: not only does he talk, but he's the president of the school's Tea Club! I swear, I don't understand some things here in the United States!

So, yeah, I tried to join the Tea Club, but Mr. Bear kept doing all these weird martial arts moves on me.

Tuns out he was trying to train me for the Tea Club Ceremonial Battle.

I can't even BEGIN to describe HOW WEIRD the whole concept is, but I knew that it really wasn't the club for me!

Now, I'm just trying to enjoy normal college life...whatever that is.

I'll tell you more about Kei (my roommate's cute friend) next time!

Love,
Hana

P.S. Can't WAIT to see you when you visit!

HANA-CHAN SOUNDS LIKE SHE'S HAVING A LOT OF FUN.

I CAN'T BELIEVE IT'S BEEN A MONTH SINCE SHE LEFT JAPAN...

WE'RE USED TO SPENDING EVERY FREE SECOND TOGETHER!

IT'S GONNA BE **AWESOME** HANGING OUT WITH HER AGAIN, EVEN THOUGH I'M ONLY VISITING FOR A FEW DAYS!

THANK YOU GRANDMA, FOR GIVING ME THIS TRIP FOR MY *EARLY CHRISTMAS* PRESENT!

ANNND....

...STILL ANOTHER *TEN HOURS* BEFORE WE LAND.

OH WELL, MIGHT AS WELL TRY TO GRAB SOME SHUT-EYE WHILE I STILL CAN.

HANA-CHAN SAID SOMETHING ABOUT HER *BIRTHDAY PARTY* A FEW HOURS AFTER I GET IN...

ZZZZ

ALLAN CITY INTERNAT

AGGAGE CLAIM

ROUND TRANSPORTATION

EXCUSE ME!

?

PARDON ME!

COMING THROUGH!

SORRY!

!

EXCUSE ME!

*TRANSLATED FROM JAPANESE.

65

⟨SO HERE'S OUR NEW STUDENT CENTER...⟩

⟨...THE COOL BOOKSTORE THAT I ALWAYS STUDY AT...⟩

⟨...AND OF COURSE, JACK FROST, THE 24-HOUR ICE CREAM JOINT!⟩

⟨KIND OF A CUTE TOWN YOU LIVE IN.⟩

⟨I THINK SO!⟩

⟨I'VE HAD MORE TIME TO ENJOY IT!⟩

⟨ESPECIALLY NOW THAT I'M OUT OF THAT SILLY TEA CLUB.⟩

...

⟨HEY... HANA-CHAN, I KNOW THAT CLUB WASN'T WHAT YOU EXPECTED.⟩

⟨STILL, THAT BEAR DIDN'T MEAN ANYTHING BY WHAT HE DID.⟩

⟨IT'S NOT LIKE YOU TO QUIT ANYTHING, NO MATTER WHAT! ARE YOU SURE IT'S O.K.?⟩

⟨I MEAN, YOU LOVE TEA MORE THAN ANYTHING!⟩

‹IT WAS...›

‹...MORE *STRESS* THAN IT WAS WORTH.›

‹I MEAN, THE PRESIDENT IS A BEAR. NOT ONLY THAT, HE PRETTY MUCH *ATTACKS* ME AT THE FIRST MEETING.›

‹THEN HE *WHISKS* ME OFF, WITHOUT EVEN ASKING ME, TO THE MOUNTAINS FOR SOME KIND OF TRAINING?! WITH *TEA*?!›

‹ALL THE WEIRDNESS, HIDDEN AGENDAS, OBLIGATIONS, EXPECTATIONS... HE *NEVER* GAVE ME A *CHOICE*.›

‹I FELT *SUFFOCATED*!›

⟨WOW! THIS IS SO COOL!⟩

...

⟨YOUR NEW FRIENDS DID ALL THIS FOR YOU?!⟩

...

⟨UM, YOU MIGHT WANNA GO THANK THEM OR SOMETHING.⟩

...

KRIS! KEI! THIS IS ALL SO BEAUTIFUL...

I HARDLY RECOGNIZE THAT THIS IS *CAFE SUA DA!*

OF COURSE IT'S BEAUTIFUL.

WE COULDN'T LET YOUR FIRST BIRTHDAY AWAY FROM HOME GO BY WITHOUT A BANG!

'S GREAT, BUT...

WHAT THE -- THIS DRESS WON'T STAY UP !!!

YOU'RE FLAT! HA HA

HA HA HA HA

I WOULD'VE WORN MINE, BUT KRIS DIDN'T *FIT* INTO HERS.

TUG.

WHERE RE THE STUMES REPARED FOR YOU GUYS?

SINCE I HAD TO SWITCH COSTUMES, I MADE *MR. SMARTY* HERE MATCH ME.

.P.D.

JAB

D'OH!

GIGGLE

TAP TAP

TAP TAP TAP TAP TAP TAP
TAP TAP TAP TAP TAP TAP TA
TAP TAP TAP TAP TAP TAP TA
TAP TAP TAP TAP TAP TA
TAP TAP TAP TAP TAP TAP
TAP TAP TAP TAP TAP TAP

71

72

UMMM...

?

OH! DON'T THINK I FORGOT ABOUT YOU! *HAPPY BIRTHDAY!*

TH- *THANK YOU,* MR. BEAR.

I HAVE TO ADMIT, I'M A LITTLE DISAPPOINTED THAT YOU GUYS DIDN'T GO WITH MY VIDEOGAME THEME..

...BUT YOU REALLY MAKE A GREAT *TEA CLUSTER!*

GASP

TEA CLUSTERS ARE HAND-SHAPED GROUPS OF TEA LEAVES, SOMETIMES RESEMBLING ANIMALS OR FLOWERS.*

YOU KNOW WHAT I AM!

*SPECIAL THANKS TO MICHAEL "SILVER NEEDLE" LERNER.

I'LL GO HELP KRIS WITH THE REST OF THE DECORATIONS ...

HERE YOU GO, KEI-SAN. PLEASE, TAKE CARE OF HER.

SURE.

...

MAYBE... HE REALLY DOES CARE ABOUT ME?

UMM... THANKS, KEI.

I'M ACTUALLY DOING O.K... NO HARM DONE.

HUH? HANA, ARE YOU SURE?

I MEAN, HE REALLY *DID* SQUEEZE YOU PRETTY HARD--

NO, I'M FINE! REALLY!

MY HEAD ACTUALLY FEELS A LOT *CLEARER* NOW.

DOES THAT MEAN YOU'RE *FINALLY* READY TO ENJOY YOUR OWN *BIRTHDAY PARTY*?

THE END!

MOM SENT ME
HER SPECIAL
GREEN TEA
FOR MY
BIRTHDAY! ♡

MY BABY GIRL
IS 18 NOW!

HALLO!

'TIS I, P.M.B.Q., HERE TO SHARE SOME INFO ABOUT A VERY SPECIAL *TEA CLUB* CHARACTER...

...MR. BEAR!

?

UZZY EARS
(THEY OFTEN WIGGLE O EXPRESS MOODS)

SMALL EYES
(NEVERTHELESS, BRIGHT AND EXPRESSIVE!)

IGHT-BROWN NOUT

LONG ARMS
(EXCELLENT FOR QUICK POKING)

FIVE "FINGER" PADS

SOFT, DARK GREY FUR
(NOT BLACK. ORIGINALLY I DID WANT MR. BEAR TO BE A BLACK BEAR, BUT THAT WOULD HAVE MADE IT HARD TO SEE HIS ARMS AND SUCH. IT WOULD ALSO TAKE UP A LOT OF BLACK INK! AS FAR AS I KNOW, THE CLOSEST REAL SPECIES OF BEAR TO BE LIKE MR. BEAR IS PROBABLY OF THE GRIZZLY SORT. GRIZZLIES DON'T HAVE LIGHT-COLORED SNOUTS, THOUGH.

CUTE BELLY

FIVE "TOE" PADS

MR. BEAR IS CLEARLY
A BEAR LIKE NO OTHER!

LET'S HEAR WHAT THE *OTHER* TEA CLUB CAST MEMBERS HAVE TO SAY ABOUT MR. BEAR...

THE DUDE BIT MY ARM.

FOR *NO* GOOD REASON.

NEED I *SAY* MORE?

HANA NEKO, TALLAN U. FRESHMAN

I THINK HE'S *AWESOME.*

DEFINITELY ONE OF THE BEST BUDS I'VE MADE HERE AT TALLAN.

KRIS TRAN, TALLAN U. SOPHOMORE

UH... HE'S ALWAYS BEEN SUPER-RESPECTFUL TO ME.

O.K. IN MY BOOK!

KEI OKUMA, TALLAN U. SOPHOMORE

LIKE THE YOUNG MAN SAID, VERY RESPECTFUL AND POLITE!

I'M ALWAYS HAPPY TO HELP HIM OUT!

MRS. HOANG, CAFE SUA DA OWNER

AND ME?

WELL, MR. BEAR GIVES SOME OF THE BEST HUGS I'VE HAD THE PLEASURE OF RECEIVING! YOU CAN'T GO WRONG WITH *GREAT* HUGS.

SEE YA NEXT TIME!

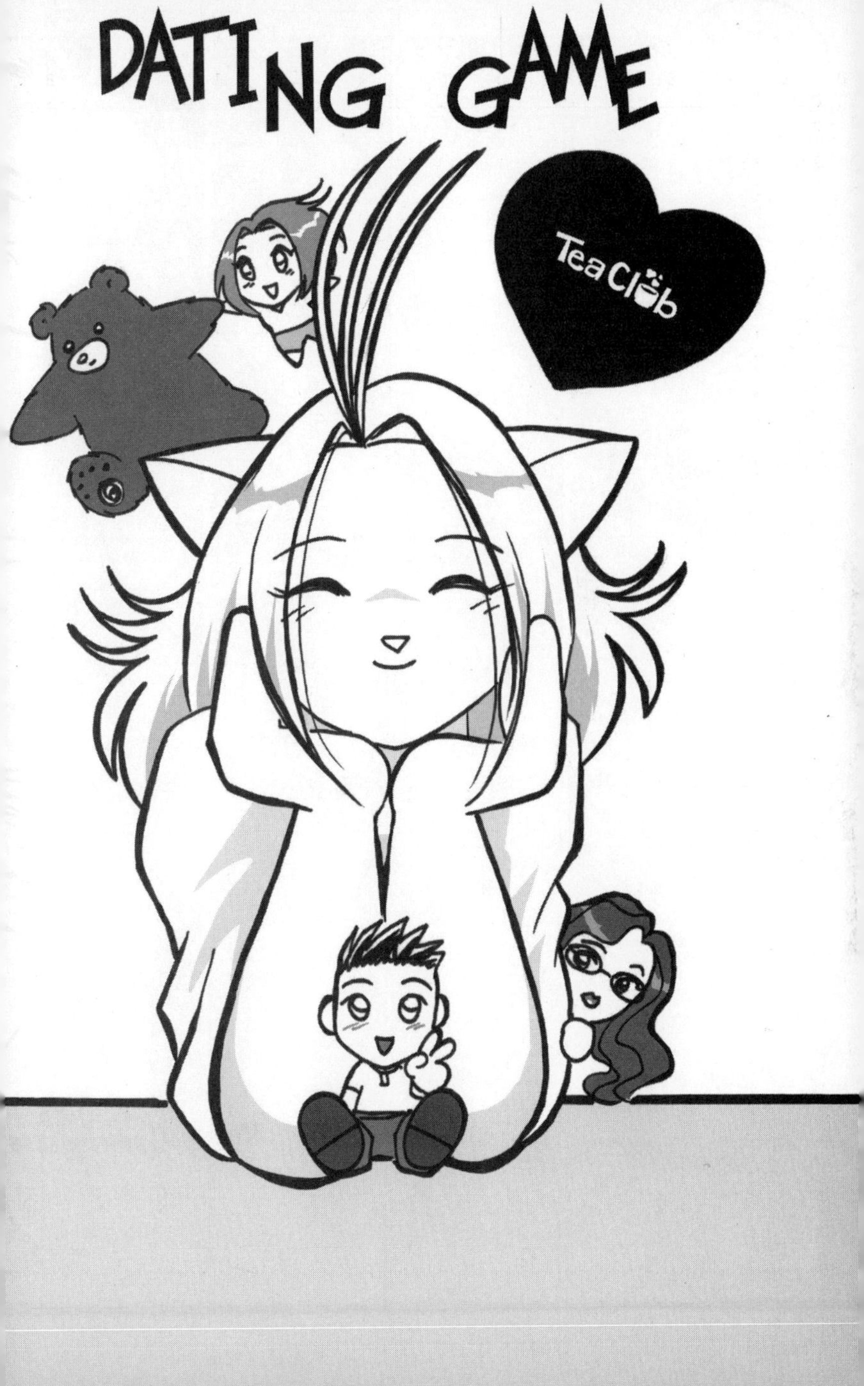
DATING GAME
Tea Club

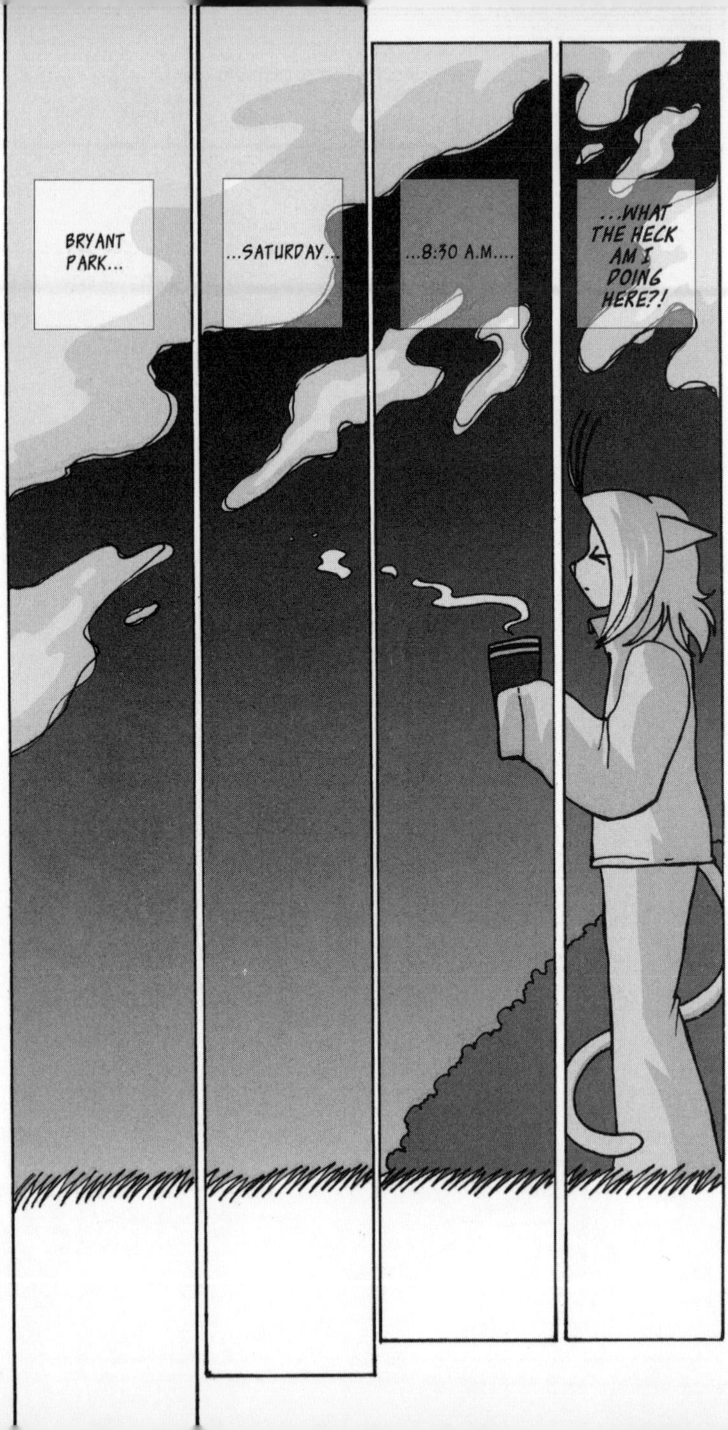
BRYANT PARK...
...SATURDAY...
...8:30 A.M....
...WHAT THE HECK AM I DOING HERE?!

WHOOSH!

OH YEAH, THAT'S RIGHT.

GO, KEI!

MY ROOMMATE, KRIS, DRAGGED ME OUT TO WATCH HER CROSS COUNTRY MEET. HER *CUTE* FRIEND, KEI, IS RUNNING, TOO.

KEI OKUMA--MY ROOMMATE'S BEST FRIEND. THE FIRST GUY I'VE MET AT TALLAN UNIVERSITY WHO SEEMS TO CLICK WITH ME. (UNLIKE A CERTAIN LARGE, FUZZY DUDE I KNOW...)

HMMM ...

...KEI'S TUSH ISN'T TOO BAD, EITHER!

AW, DID I JUST MISS THEM?

!

I'M SORRY.

DIDN'T MEAN TO STARTLE YOU!

WOW, SHE'S REALLY PRETTY!

OH, IT'S O.K.! NO WORRIES!

HI, I'M ATSUKO.

NICE TO MEET YOU, ATSUKO! MY NAME IS HANA.

SO I JUST MISSED THEM, HUH?

DON'T WORRY, THEY'LL BE BACK ONCE THEY FINISH THE HILLY LOOP.

WOW, IT'S NICE TO RUN INTO A FELLOW CROSS COUNTRY FAN!

WELL, I'M REALLY JUST HERE FOR A *FRIEND*...

(I'M NOT REALLY A FAN OF *CROSS COUNTRY*, EXACTLY!)

*TRANSLATED FROM JAPANESE.

*FROM THE COUNTRY OF FELIS! YEP, THAT'S PART OF THIS WORLD. --PMBQ.

90

YEP, I REALLY SMOKED THAT ONE WELLINGTON TECH GIRL (UH, NO OFFENSE, ATSUKO). MAN, SHE TRIED TO ELBOW ME AND STUFF, BUT I SHOWED *HER* AT THE END!

EVEN GOT A PERSONAL RECORD ON THE COURSE TODAY...

BLAHBLAHBLAHBLAHBLAHBLAHBLAHBLAHBLAHBLAHBLAHBLAHBLAHBLAHBLAHBLAHBLAHBLAHBLAH

PSST! KEI! IS KRIS ALWAYS LIKE THIS AFTER A RACE?!

I HATE TO SAY IT, BUT YEAH.

BY THE WAY, IT WAS REALLY SWEET OF YOU TO COME TO THE MEET TODAY! THANKS!

OH, IT WAS NOTHING...

...REALLY.

BLUSH!

...

AND DID YOU SEE THE WAY I--

MUNCH

MR. BEAR! YOU ALWAYS HAVE GREAT TIMING!

HULLO, EVERYONE!

HEY GUYS, IT'S TIME FOR ME TO HEAD OUT.

IT'S BEEN FUN MEETING ALL OF YOU, THOUGH!

AWWW, DO YOU HAVE TO GO SO SOON?

YEAH... A TON OF HOMEWORK IS WAITING FOR ME AT HOME.

WELL, I HAD A LOT OF FUN HANGING OUT AT THE MEET! I HOPE WE CAN DO SOMETHING TOGETHER AGAIN, SOON!

YOU HAVE MY NUMBER, RIGHT?

YEAH! I'LL DEFINITELY GIVE YOU A CALL SOMETIME.

SEE YOU ALL LATER!

BYE, ATSUKO!

HEY, SHE CAN'T LEAVE! I'M NOT DONE WITH MY STORY!

...

SHUT *UP*, KRIS.

HANA-CHAN*, ARE YOU FREE TONIGHT? I'D LIKE TO TAKE YOU OUT AS THANKS FOR COMING TODAY.

HA! YOU KNOW HOW HARD IT WAS FOR ME TO GET HER UP AT 6 A.M.?!

I-- I'D LOVE TO, KEI-KUN*!

*"-CHAN" AND "-KUN" ARE SORTA LIKE TERMS OF ENDEARMENT/FAMILIARITY IN JAPANESE--PMBQ.

A DATE WITH KEI! A DATE WITH KEI! A DATE WITH KEI! A DATE WITH KEI!

BUT... WHAT ABOUT ME, KEI? AREN'T I YOUR ONE AND ONLY?!

GIRL, YOU KNOW I TAKE YOU OUT ALL THE TIME.

FEAR NOT, KRIS. I SHALL TAKE YOU OUT FOR DINNER TONIGHT.

REALLY?!

IT BETTER NOT BE OUT TO THE FOREST FOR HONEYCOMB... LIKE LAST TIME.

I'LL PICK YOU UP AT 7!

YAY!

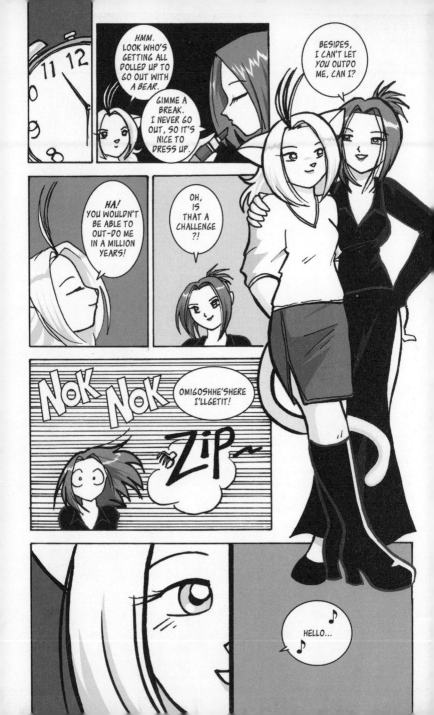

WOW!

I THOUGHT YOU MIGHT BE TIRED OF DORM FOOD...

I... I DON'T KNOW WHERE TO START!

DIG IN WHILE IT'S STILL HOT!

AHRM.

MUNCH *MUNCH*

WHEN I MISS "HOMESTYLE" COOKING, I LIKE TO COME HERE.

THIS IS FANTASTIC. THANK YOU, KEI!

*SEE TEA CLUB #2 --PMBG.

I KNEW WHEN WE FIRST MET THAT ATUSKO WAS PRETTY ...

... BUT SHE'S REALLY *GORGEOUS* WHEN SHE'S DRESSED UP.

I WONDER.

DOES KEI LIKE *HER* MORE THAN *ME?*

I'M ACTUALLY ON MY WAY TO MEET MY BOYFRIEND, BUT I SAW YOU GUYS THROUGH THE WINDOW.

JUST WANTED TO SAY "HI," EVEN THOUGH WE ALREADY HUNG OUT EARLIER...

I'M SURE WE'LL RUN INTO EACH OTHER MORE OFTEN!

OUR SCHOOLS ARE PRETTY CLOSE.

HEY, MAYBE WE CAN HAVE DINNER HERE SOMETIME!

THIS PLACE IS *GREAT!*

KEI OR NOT, SHE'S *STILL* MY FRIEND.

NOW *THAT* SOUNDS LIKE A GREAT PLAN.

WHOA, IS IT 8:00 ALREADY?! I BETTER GO AND MEET CRAIG!

SEE YOU TWO LATER! CALL ME, O.K., HANA-CHAN?

SMEK

HWoooooooooooooo ~ ..

ATSUKO IS MY *FRIEND*. I *THOUGHT* SHE KNEW THAT I LIKED KEI.

SHE HAS A BOYFRIEND, BUT SHE JUST KISSED HIM! (IT WAS JUST ON THE CHEEK, BUT STILL!)

IF SHE WANTS KEI, HOW CAN I COMPETE?!

NO! SHE WOULDN'T DO THAT TO ME!

WOULD SHE?

HANA-CHAN! ARE YOU DONE?

I... I THINK SO.

IT'S STILL EARLY!

WANNA CATCH A MOVIE?

MY TREAT!

THAT SOUNDS GREAT!

I'VE BEEN WANTING TO SEE THIS...

KRIS *HATES* THESE KINDS OF MOVIES!

TOTALLY HER LOSS!

AND MY GAIN, HEH.

CINEMA

LAST SHOT 2
PEACH FUZZ
NOW PLAYING

HMMM...

MAYBE NOW'S THE TIME TO MAKE A MOVE...

HANA! ARE YOU O.K.?

ALL RIGHT, WHO'S THE JERK THAT--

--DID THAT...

OH NO! HANA!

I TAKE IT YOU KNOW MY GIRLFRIEND, THE CLUTZ.

I'M SORRY, DEAR! IT JUST SLIPPED!

IT'S O.K. ...

WE'VE STILL GOT TIME TO CLEAN YOU UP.

ATSUKO, CAN YOU SAVE OUR SEATS?

OF COURSE!

AND SO, THE MOVIE WENT ON WITHOUT A HITCH ...

HEY, BUY THAT SHOE AND YOU CAN OUTRUN THE SHADOWGUNNER!

WOW, REALLY?!

... SORT OF.

ZZZ

...

SO, SHE'S HERE WITH HER BOYFRIEND, BUT SHE FELL ASLEEP ON KEI'S SHOULDER.

I GUESS THAT CAN BE NORMAL.

ZZZZZZ.

SIGH

I CAN'T HELP IT. I'M JEALOUS! THERE'S NO RISING ABOVE IT.

PSST! WANNA CUT OUT OF HERE EARLY?

!

zip!

OH, KEI!

WHAT?

HOW DID YOU KNOW?!

BLACK PEARL TEA IS ONE OF MY FAVORITES! *DROOL*

KRIS TOLD ME.

SHE SAID, "IF ANYTHING CHEERS UP HANEKO, IT'S GOTTA BE BLACK PEARL TEA!"

I KNOW SHE TEASES YOU A LOT, BUT SHE REALLY LIKES YOU.

SHE CARES ABOUT YOU, YA KNOW?

SIP

HMMM...

WHAT ABOUT YOU, KEI-KUN?

HUH?

DO YOU CARE ABOUT ME?

UM...

WELL, I THOUGHT IT WAS KIND OF OBVIOUS--

BAM!

WHAT IS GOING ON?!

MMM♡

OH, HANA-CHAN, SORRY..

SNIFF

I...I JUST FEEL SO EMOTIONAL RIGHT NOW...

KEI'S KIND WORDS JUST SET SOMETHING OFF IN ME...

...POOR THING...

ATSUKO. I--

MAYBE...

SHAKE. SHAKE.

I DON'T BUY IT ANYMORE, ATSUKO.

THIS IS THE *THIRD* TIME YOU'VE RUN INTO US... TOO MUCH TO BE ANOTHER "COINCIDENCE" !!!

I MAY BE JUST A FRESHMAN, BUT I'M NOT AS NAIVE AS YOU THINK!

WHAT DO YOU WANT?

HEH.

I SUPPOSE I *HAVE* UNDERESTIMATED YOU, HANA NEKO.

WE MIGHT HAVE BEEN FRIENDS...

...IF YOU HADN'T BEEN HAND-PICKED BY THE *BEAR*.

?

BEAR? YOU MEAN *MISTER BEAR?!*

CAN'T SEE...

KEI... ARE YOU ALL RIGHT?

COUGH COUGH

AND WHAT *OTHER* BEAR MIGHT YOU KNOW?!

FOM

GRAB.

POOR REFLEXES! TOTALLY UNAWARE!

THIS WAS TOO EASY... I WONDER WHAT HE SEES IN YOU.

NO MATTER. TALLAN'S TEA CLUB WILL BE WEAK THIS YEAR ...

WHAT A BEAUTIFUL WAY TO FINISH MY COLLEGE CAREER, WITH A *TEA CLUB CHAMPIONSHIP* FOR WELLINGTON TECH!

111

115

NNNGH...

I KNEW THAT GIRL WAS CREEPY!

WHAT THE HECK WAS THAT ALL ABOUT, MR. B?

I DON'T KNOW WHAT HER PROBLEM IS...

STUPID NINJA GIRL! BIG MESS AND NO TIP!

SWEEP SWEEP

ATSUKO IS THE PRESIDENT OF THE WELLINGTON TECH TEA CLUB. THEY HAPPEN TO BE OUR BIGGEST RIVALS IN *CEREMONIAL BATTLE* COMPETITION.

WE'VE FACED EACH OTHER MANY TIMES, BUT AS FAR AS I KNOW WE'VE *NEVER LOST*.

WHOA, COOL.

...HM?

NEVER LOST?

UNFORTUNATELY, SINCE MOST OF THE MEMBERS GRADUATED LAST YEAR, OUR TEA CLUB ROSTER IS A BIT SPARSE.

WORD MUST'VE GOTTEN OUT ABOUT THAT, SO ALL THE SCHOOLS ARE LOOKING TO BEAT US THIS SEASON.

YOU DON'T MEAN... YOU'RE THE *ONLY* MEMBER NOW?

I AM.

BUT HEY! I'M STILL *RECRUITING*! HOW ABOUT YOU AND KEI QUIT THAT *SILLY* RUNNING TEAM AND LEARN SOME MORE ABOUT TEA?!

NO, THANK YOU.

...ORRY, ...MR. B. ...LOVE ...NNING, ...AND I ...HOULD ...SH OUT ...THE ...EASON.

YOU UNDERSTAND, RIGHT?

ARE YOU *SURE*?!

THAT *DOESN'T* WORK ON ME.

HUG

I *DID* HAVE A LOVELY EVENING WITH YOU, THOUGH.

AND I, AS WELL.

I SUPPOSE I'D BETTER PREPARE MY TRAINING SCHEDULE. HAVE TO BE READY FOR WHATEVER ATSUKO'S GOT FOR ME.

GOOD LUCK WITH THAT.

117

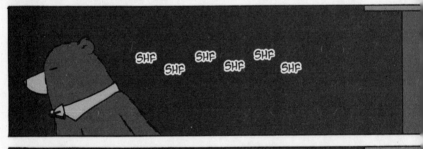

118

MR. BEAR!

HANEKO! YOU'RE LOOKING BETTER ALREADY!

YEAH, THANKS TO YOU.

SHF

SHF

OH, JUST CONSIDER US TRULY EVEN, NOW!

PAT. PAT.

...

UM...

O.K., THIS MIGHT SOUND WEIRD.

AND YOU CAN SAY "NO" IF YOU WANT TO.

?

CAN I...

...REJOIN THE TEA CLUB?

AND WHAT EXACTLY IS THAT LOOK FOR?!

IT'S NO PARTY EVERY MEETING, YOU KNOW.

I KNOW.

NO CUTE BOYS IN THE CLUB.

THAT DOESN'T MATTER.

THERE'S VIGOROUS TRAINING INVOLVED.

I'M READY.

YOUR GRADES MIGHT DROP... THIS TAKES A LOT OF TIME.

I DON'T CARE--

LOOK!

I'M SORRY. I'VE BEEN WRONG-- I MISJUDGED YOU. BUT THAT'S ALL IN THE PAST, RIGHT?

I WANT TO HELP YOU NOW!

121

123

KIDS, PLEASE DON'T TRY THIS AT HOME! ;) --PMBG

124

125

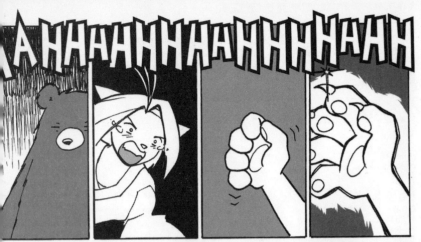

TOSS

AAHHHHHH!

CLAWS! WOW, THAT WAS A GOOD MOVE.

WHUMP

COOLED OFF YET?

WHUH... WHUZZ FORRR

...

JUST THE BEGINNING OF YOUR TRAINING.

SORRY YOU HAD TO LEARN THE HARD WAY, BUT THERE'S NO EASY WAY TO UNDERSTAND...

PERFORMING TEA CEREMONY ISN'T THE MOST IMPORTANT PART OF CERMONIAL BATTLE. KEEPING A LEVEL HEAD IN ALL SITUATIONS IS ACTUALLY A BIG KEY TO VICTORY.

WE'VE GOT TO LEARN TO CONTROL THAT HOT HEAD OF YOURS!

WHO'RE YOU CALLING HOT-HEADED, YOU BIG MEAN BEAR ?!

THERE YOU GO AGAIN.

THAT'S EXACTLY WHAT ATSUKO WANTS, YOU KNOW?

CLANK!

SHE'LL DISRUPT YOUR TEA CEREMONY BY PROVOKING YOUR *EMOTIONAL SIDE*!

WE'LL LOSE THE MATCH *RIGHT AWAY* IF YOU CAN'T STAY CALM.

YOU MEAN *I'M* GOING TO BE THE ONE TO PERFORM A *TEA CEREMONY*, WHILE ATSUKO ATTACKS ME?!

RIGHT!

I DON'T KNOW ABOUT THIS!

ISN'T THERE ANY *OTHER* WAY I CAN HELP YOU IN THE TEA CLUB? WOULDN'T WE BE BETTER OFF IF *YOU* FACED ATSUKO INSTEAD?

YOU'VE ALWAYS BEAT HER AND ALL. MORE EXPERIENCED THAN ME!

HANA NEKO.

LOTS OF GOOD THINGS ABOUT YOU. YOU'RE SMART, GREAT NATURAL ABILITIES, AND YOU LOVE TEA. I'M REALLY GLAD THAT YOU DECIDED TO REJOIN.

THANK YOU!

PAT.

THERE'S ONE *BIG THING* YOU NEED TO WORK ON, THOUGH ...

WHAT'S THAT?

SOMETIMES YOU NEED TO SHUT UP, LISTEN, AND DO AS YOU'RE TOLD.

LOOK, I *ONLY* WANT YOU TO BE HERE IF YOU'RE PREPARED TO DO *WHATEVER IT TAKES* TO BECOME A TEA CLUB WARRIOR.

EEP!

FOR *WHATEVER* REASON, YOU'VE ASKED ME TO COME BACK INTO THE CLUB.

DON'T WASTE MY TIME IF YOU'RE NOT GOING TO EVEN *TRY* TO LISTEN TO WHAT I HAVE TO TEACH!

....

MY REASON FOR RE-JOINING ....

KICK KICK KICK KICK

HEE HEE HEE HEE HEE

HANEKO! YOU'RE SO COOL FOR BEATING ATSUKO!

I'M SORRY THAT I ALWAYS MAKE FUN OF YOU! HOW CAN I MAKE IT UP TO YOU?!

WELL... DO MY LAUNDRY FOR THE REST OF THE SEMESTER AND WE'LL CALL IT EVEN.

DONE!

KEI-KUN!

OH, HANA-CHAN.

I LOVE YOU EVEN MORE, NOW THAT YOU'VE KICKED THE CRAP OUT OF THAT FLOOZY, ATSUKO!

KISS ME, MY DARLING!

HARUMPH

HE'S STILL IN **HUGE MODE!**

AHEH

SORRY FOR BEING UNFOCUSED, MR. BEAR.

I AM...

READY TO BECOME YOUR DISCIPLE!

KSHAHHHH!

YOU KNOW, YOU'VE KEPT THAT TEAPOT ON YOUR HEAD THIS WHOLE TIME WITHOUT A PROBLEM!

OH! I DIDN'T EVEN NOTICE!

I GUESS I'M STARTING TO GET THE HANG OF THIS--

OVERHEAT

-RIGHT?

IT REALLY IS QUITE HOT. *PLEASE DON'T DO THIS AT H*

EYAHHHHHHH!

SOUNDS LIKE THE TEA CLUB HAS A NEW MEMBER.

DUDE, I'D *NEVER* JOIN THAT CLUB!

AND SO THE DAYS PASS...

AIR, EARTH, TOIL AND SWEAT

IN ALL THINGS IT IS HIDDEN--

FIND THE WAY OF TEA.

--HAIKU BY MR. BEAR

134

135

IT'S *BEAUTIFUL*!

CEREMONIAL BATTLE *IS BASED* ON TRADITIONAL JAPANESE TEA CEREMONY...

YOU NEED SUITABLE CLOTHES FOR YOUR DEBUT!

THANK YOU, MR. BEAR!

I LOVE IT!

SHUCKS.

*JAPANESE SUFFIX USED TO ADDRESS CLOSE FRIENDS OR SMALL CHILDREN

〈WHAT DO YOU WANT, ATSUKO?〉*

〈YOU'RE NOT *STILL* MAD FROM THE OTHER DAY, ARE YOU? I WAS JUST JOKING AROUND!〉

〈RIGHT. BETRAYING AND ATTACKING ME**, WHAT A FUNNY JOKE.〉

〈COME NOW, I *REALLY* WANTED TO SEE HOW YOU'VE BEEN DOING!〉

〈OH! IS THAT YOUR *BATTLE KIMONO*?!〉

〈CAN I SEE?〉

〈CAN I SEE?〉

〈CAN I SEE?〉

**READ THE *EXCITING* ISSUE OF *TEA CLUB* #3!--PMBQ

〈JUST A PEAK AT THE PATTERN ...〉

GRAB.

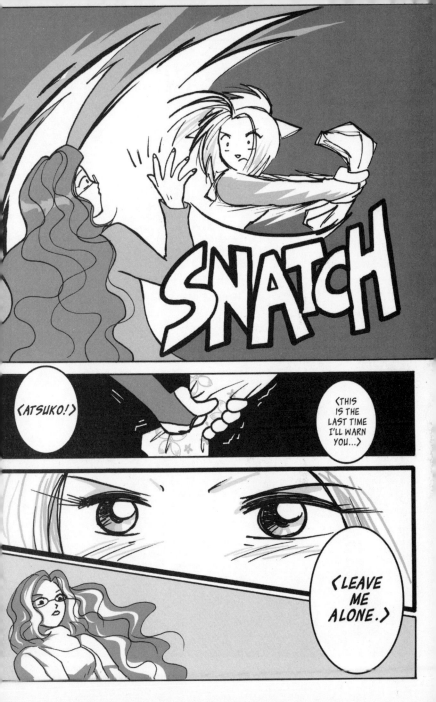

TO BE CONTINUE

I LOOK FORWARD
TO THEIR BATTLE.

THIS BLACK PEARL TEA....
...IT'S *PERFECT*...

YAHOO!

145

...

SIGH

DOES THAT MEAN THAT YOU'RE STILL AN UNDECLARED COLLEGE MAJOR?

SHUT UP!

WHAT'S THE BIG DEAL, ANYWAY? I'M ONLY 19. WHY'S IT SO IMPORTANT FOR ME TO FIND MY LIFE'S PURPOSE SO SOON, HUH? WHAT'S SO GREAT ABOUT WORKING SOME LAME RATRACE JOB FOR 50% OF MY LIFE...WHO'S IN A HURRY TO GET TO *THAT*?!

AND WHAT'S WRONG WITH JUST LIKING RUNNING?

MY PARENTS HAVE BEEN ON MY CASE ALL SUMMER ABOUT THIS STUFF, AND NOW *YOU*--

KRIS.

I'M SORRY. I DIDN'T MEAN ANYTHING.

149

SIGHHHHHHHHH

?

〈HOW SAD...〉*

〈OUR BABY HANA-CHAN...〉

〈YOU'RE LEAVING US SO SOON!!〉

AHHHHHHHH!

〈MOM...DAD.〉

〈YOU KNOW THAT THIS IS THE BEST THING FOR MY FUTURE.〉

〈I'M GOING TO STUDY HARD AT TALLAN, AND BECOME THE BEST PHYSICAL TRAINER EVER!〉

NSLATED FROM JAPANESE.

HANDA & RIN-CHAN,
WARRIORS FROM THE
VIDEOGAME "MIGHTY FIST"
(YES, I MADE IT UP)

Tea Club side story: FRIENDSHIP

SIP.

⟨ADMIT IT. I ALMOST HAD YOU THAT TIME.⟩*

VICTORY HANDA!

⟨LOOK AT HOW CLOSE THOSE HEALTH BARS ARE!⟩

⟨IF IT WEREN'T FOR HANDA'S *CHEAP THROWS....* SHEESH!⟩

⟨MANAMI-CHAN, DON'T BE SUCH A SORE LOSER! YOU NEED TO SAVOR THESE MEMORIES.⟩

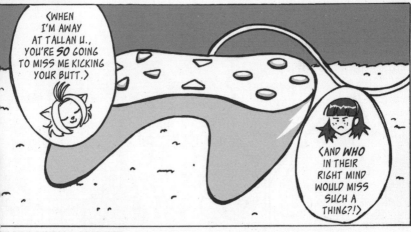

⟨WHEN I'M AWAY AT TALLAN U., YOU'RE *SO* GOING TO MISS ME KICKING YOUR BUTT.⟩

⟨AND *WHO* IN THEIR RIGHT MIND WOULD MISS SUCH A THING?!⟩

*TRANSLATED FROM JAPANESE.

Thank you for reading *Tea Club*!

Both online and offline,
it's been a labor of love for me.

This is the first of hopefully many volumes;
I intend to continue writing and drawing this story
until it's finished. I have an idea of what that end
will be like, but for now I'm focusing on
(and enjoying) the journey.

I raise my cup, in hopes that
you'll be along for the ride!

for news, more comics, and volume two info, visit

http://www.teaclubcomic.com